All illustrations by the Disney Storybook Art Team
Published by Disney Press, an imprint of Disney Book Group.
For information address Disney Press, 1200 Grand Central Avenue, Glendale, California 91201.
This special edition was printed for Kohl's Department Stores, Inc.
(for distribution on behalf of Kohl's Cares, LLC, its wholly owned subsidiary),
by Disney Press, an imprint of Disney Book Group, Los Angeles/New York.

Kohl's
Style Number 9781368028585
Factory Number 131635
06/18-08/18

Printed in the United States of America

First Hardcover Edition, August 2018
1 3 5 7 9 10 8 6 4 2
FAC-131635-18222
ISBN 978-1-368-02858-5

For more Disney Press fun, visit disneybooks.com

CONTENTS

CHEF MICKEY

Mickey was excited. He was cooking a romantic dinner for Minnie. He wanted everything to be perfect. There was just one problem. . . . Mickey didn't know what to make!

Maybe my friends will have some ideas, Mickey thought.

Mickey called Donald and Goofy. The friends agreed to come over and help.

Soon Donald and Goofy arrived. They had brought Daisy to help, too!

"What should I make?" Mickey asked his friends.

"Hmmm . . . Minnie likes lasagna," said Daisy.

Daisy was right. Minnie *loved* lasagna. Mickey nodded and started to gather the ingredients.

But Donald had a different idea. "You should make a turkey," he said. "It's Minnie's favorite. That will show her how well you know her!"

"How about a salad?" Goofy added.

Mickey was confused. Daisy was right, but Donald was right, too. And a salad *did* sound good. What was he going to do?

Mickey looked at the ingredients he had taken out. What if he chose wrong?

"What do you think I should do, Pluto?" he asked.

"Woof, woof," Pluto barked.

"You're right," Mickey said. "I *should* make them all!"

Soon Mickey was busy making turkey *and* lasagna *and* salad. It was a lot of food, but he was sure Minnie would love it!

Mickey looked at the clock. It was getting late! He still needed to set the table, but he was too busy cooking.

"I can help you, Mickey," Daisy said.

Daisy pulled out plates and glasses. Then she set the table, decorating it in all Minnie's favorite colors.

Meanwhile, Goofy prepared a special fruit punch.

"Gawrsh, this is fun!" he said, spilling punch all over the table as he stirred.

Finally, the drink was ready. Goofy picked up the punch bowl and headed to the dining room. He didn't see Donald walking by with the salad.

CRASH!

Goofy and Donald smacked into each other. Salad flew into the air. Punch spilled all over the floor. And Goofy fell into Daisy's beautiful table.

Hearing all the noise, Mickey raced into the dining room. He could barely believe his eyes. Everyone's hard work was ruined!

"I'm sorry, Mickey," Goofy said. "I didn't mean to ruin everything. I just wanted to help."

"Me, too," Donald said. "I wanted everything to be perfect!"

Mickey looked at his sad friends. "It's okay," he said. "I know it was an accident."

With his friends' help, Mickey began to clean up the mess. Suddenly, he sniffed the air. "Does anyone smell something burning?" Mickey asked.

Mickey opened the oven. He had been so busy cleaning that he had forgotten all about the food. Everything was overcooked!

The dining room was still a mess, and now the food was ruined, too. What was Mickey going to do?

Just then, Minnie walked through the door. "Hi, Mickey," she called sweetly. "I'm here for our special night."

Minnie looked around the messy room. Mickey was holding a burned turkey, her friends were covered in food, and the table was a mess!

"Oh, Mickey. What happened?" Minnie asked.

"I had everything planned out," Mickey told Minnie. "I wanted our night to be special, so I made all your favorite dishes—turkey, lasagna, and salad. I even asked Goofy and Donald to help out. But then Goofy dropped the punch, and Donald dropped the salad. After that, I guess things just got out of control."

"It's okay, Mickey," Minnie said. "I love that you wanted everything to be perfect, but that's not what's important. What's important is the time we spend together."

"Aw, shucks, Minnie," Mickey said. "Thanks! But what are we going to do about dinner?"

Minnie smiled. "I have an idea," she said.

Mickey looked at Minnie and smiled. His night wasn't what he had expected, but he was still having fun. And he had learned an important lesson. As long as he was with Minnie, nothing else mattered.

Mickey handed Minnie a slice of pizza. "You're right, Minnie," he said. "This *is* the perfect night after all."

GONE SURFIN'

It was a perfect day for the beach. The sun was shining, and the water was crystal clear.

Mickey and his friends climbed out of the car and unloaded their surfboards. Goofy was going to teach everyone how to surf!

Mickey couldn't wait to get started. As he looked out at the crashing waves, he pictured himself gliding across them.

"Come on! Let's go!" Mickey called, running into the water.

Boards in hand, Minnie, Donald, and Daisy raced after him.

Goofy chased his friends, the hot sand burning his feet.

"Ooh! Ouch! Wait up," Goofy cried. "Where are you going?"

Donald looked at Goofy, confused. "What do you mean?" he asked.
"We're going to surf!"

"Hyuck," Goofy laughed. "Not yet. You have to learn the basics on
the sand. Come on, I'll show you!"

With Goofy's help, the friends practiced paddling on their surfboards. Then Goofy showed them how to pop up when they reached a wave. But as he leaped up to stand, he lost his balance!

"Whoa!" Goofy cried. He flailed his arms and toppled off the side of his board. "Gawrsh," he said with a laugh, brushing off sand. "That sure was a big wave!"

Lying on her stomach, Minnie placed her hands under her. Then, pushing off, she jumped to stand up on her board, one leg in front of the other.

Goofy clapped. "Good job, Minnie!" he said.

Before long, Donald and Daisy learned to pop up, too. "This is too easy!" Donald complained. "When do we get to go into the water?"

But Mickey wasn't finding it easy at all. He kept losing his balance and falling off his board!

Mickey wiped sweat from his brow. "Gosh, Goof. This is harder than it looks!" he said. "I keep falling over."

"That's okay, Mickey," Goofy said. "Falling is part of surfing. Try this!"

Goofy showed Mickey how to get on his knees on the surfboard before popping up. Pretty soon, Mickey got the hang of it.

"Way to go!" Minnie said, patting him on the back.

Meanwhile, Donald was getting more and more impatient. "Surfing on sand is boring!" he said, stomping his foot. "I want to go in the water!"

Goofy looked out at the ocean. "I'm ready if you are!" he said. "Let's catch some waves!"

But surfing was much harder on water than on sand. Donald tried to surf a wave . . . and plunged into the ocean.

Just when Daisy thought she was surfing—*splash!*—she tumbled into the ocean, too. "Ptooey!" She spit water from her beak.

Minnie was the first to find her balance. Her friends cheered as she crested a wave. After a while, Daisy shakily got up on her board, too. "Cowabunga!" she exclaimed.

Donald was tired of crashing. "This is taking forever!" he said. But finally, he rode a wave, too. "I'm doing it!" he said before tipping back into the water.

Meanwhile, Mickey wasn't having very much luck. He couldn't stay on his board! Every time he popped up, he toppled over and wiped out!

"Phew!" said Mickey. He needed a break! Learning to surf wasn't easy, but Mickey wasn't going to give up.

Just then, Goofy floated by, relaxing on his board and soaking up the rays.

"Hey, Goof," Mickey called. "I'm having a little trouble! How about some one-on-one help?"

"Of course, Mickey!" Goofy said. "That's what friends are for!"

"Thanks!" Mickey said.

"I know just how you feel. When I started surfing, I didn't think I'd ever figure it out!" Goofy said. "I still fall sometimes. But so does every surfer!"

Mickey took Goofy's words to heart. He was up for the challenge!

Goofy and Mickey practiced paddling. They practiced popping up. They even practiced keeping their balance on the board.

Soon Mickey saw a big wave headed his way. He paddled toward the wave, and before he knew it . . .

. . . he was surfing!

Mickey's friends clapped and cheered.

"You're doing it!" Minnie shouted.

"Hooray!" yelled Donald and Daisy.

Goofy was celebrating loudest of all. "I knew you could do it, Mickey!" he shouted.

Mickey loved the feeling of surfing! It was just like he'd imagined. Learning hadn't been easy, but the hard work had been worth it. And having friends to cheer him on made it that much sweeter!

A DAY AT THE PARK

One sunny afternoon, Mickey and his nephews headed to Wonder World, the best amusement park around. For weeks Morty and Ferdie had been begging their uncle to take them.

"Here it is, boys!" said Mickey. "Are you ready for a day full of rides and games?"

"Yes!" the boys shouted together. They could hardly wait to get through the gates!

"Wait until you try out the bumper cars," Mickey said as they walked into the park. "They're my favorite ride here! Now come on. What should we do first?"

"I'm going right to the teacups!" said Ferdie excitedly.

"I'm going right to the swings!" Morty said, jumping up and down.

Mickey laughed. "Well, we can't do two things at the same time, so let's—"

But Morty and Ferdie weren't listening. The two ran off in opposite directions!

"Boys! Boys! Come back!" Mickey yelled after them. But the boys were already too far away to hear him.

Mickey ran after
Morty, but his nephew was
already out of sight. Where could
he have gone? What had he said he wanted to do first?

"The swings!" Mickey said, running toward the ride.

Mickey craned his neck, trying to see if Morty was on the ride. It
was way above his head, going around and around. All he could see
were feet! He watched for a few minutes, but he didn't think he saw
his nephew.

I guess I'll go look for Ferdie, Mickey thought.

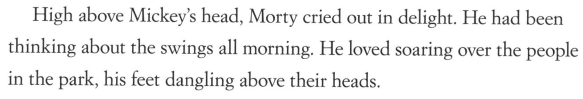

High above Mickey's head, Morty cried out in delight. He had been thinking about the swings all morning. He loved soaring over the people in the park, his feet dangling above their heads.

Suddenly, Morty spotted his uncle Mickey.

"Hi, Uncle Mickey!" he shouted. But he was too far up for his uncle to hear him.

As Mickey ran to the other side of the park, he tried to remember what Ferdie had wanted to do. Then he spotted them: the teacups!

Mickey watched as the giant cups spun around and around. He looked into each cup as it passed by him, but he didn't see Ferdie anywhere. And just watching the ride was making Mickey dizzy! He decided to try another direction.

Where should I look next? he thought.

Inside a teacup, Ferdie grabbed the wheel in the middle. He pulled hard to spin himself around faster and faster. *Whoosh* went the wind across his face as he whipped around. Ferdie laughed. He wished Morty and Uncle Mickey were there to join in the fun!

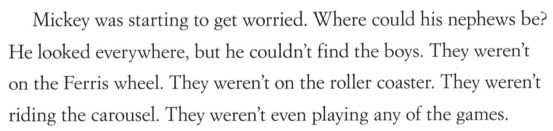

Mickey was starting to get worried. Where could his nephews be? He looked everywhere, but he couldn't find the boys. They weren't on the Ferris wheel. They weren't on the roller coaster. They weren't riding the carousel. They weren't even playing any of the games.

Finally, Mickey stumbled upon a huge crowd of
people. *What's going on?* he wondered. He peeked
through the people and saw a parade winding
down the path. There were floats, a marching band,
dancers . . . even clowns.

Morty and Ferdie would never miss this! he
thought. He began to search for them in the crowd.
But the boys were nowhere to be found.

Mickey glumly sat down on a bench and watched people walking by. Suddenly, he heard someone calling his name.

"Uncle Mickey!"

Morty and Ferdie, loaded down with snacks, ran up to Mickey.

"We've been looking for you everywhere!" said Morty. "Where were you?"

Mickey jumped up and pulled the boys into a huge hug. "*You* were looking for *me*?" he said. "I looked for you all over the park!"

"We're sorry," said Ferdie.

"We were just so excited to try all the rides!" said Morty. "We've done just about everything."

"I was hoping we'd explore the park *together*," said Mickey. "That's part of the fun of coming here."

"Sorry, Uncle Mickey," the boys said. Then they looked at each other and smiled.

"We did save the best part for you, though," said Morty.

Crash! Mickey's bumper car bounced off Ferdie's and straight into Morty's.

"I'll get you for that!" yelled Morty, steering back toward his uncle. Mickey drove his car out of the way, causing Morty to bump into Ferdie instead. All three of them laughed.

"You were right, Uncle Mickey," said Ferdie.

"Yep! It's way more fun to do this together!" agreed Morty.

Mickey smiled and drove his car right into his nephews' cars—*BONK!*

MICKEY'S RAFTING TRIP

One sunny summer's day, Mickey, Minnie, and Pluto headed deep into the woods.

"I can't wait to get to the river," Minnie said. "Going white-water rafting is such an adventure!"

Pluto barked in agreement.

"Well, you don't have to wait much longer," Mickey said, pointing through the trees. "Look! There's the river!"

When they reached the water, Mickey inflated the raft while
Pluto unpacked the oars. Minnie secured all their gear for the trip
downriver. Then the three friends put on their helmets and climbed
into the raft. The water was shallow and still.

"One, two, three, push!" Mickey yelled. He and Minnie pushed
away from the shore with their oars. Then they paddled through the
calm water toward the rapids.

When they reached the fast-moving water, Mickey and Minnie worked together to move the raft safely through the choppy waves.

"Paddle on the left!" Minnie yelled to Mickey over the roaring river.

Mickey moved his oar to the left side and pulled it hard through the water. The little raft veered around a rock.

Pluto sat in the middle of the raft, watching the forest rush by and loving the ride.

The trio swished and bumped and sloshed their way down the river. Suddenly, Pluto stood and started barking.

"What is it, boy?" Mickey asked. He and Minnie both looked in the direction that Pluto was barking.

"Oh, Mickey, look! There's a bear cub stuck on that rock!" cried Minnie.

Just ahead of them, a sopping wet bear cub stood shivering on a large rock in the middle of the river. He looked cold and scared.

"We have to help him!" Minnie said. "But the raft is headed away from him."

"Quick!" Mickey said. "Paddle on the right!"

The two friends pulled their oars hard, turning the raft toward the little bear.

Mickey jumped out and pulled the raft near the rock.

"Hi, little guy," he said, turning to the bear cub. "How did you get stuck out here?"

"Bears like to swim," Minnie said. "Maybe this cub is too young to be a strong swimmer, and the current pulled him out here."

"Let's get him in the raft. We'll take him back to the shore to find his family," Mickey said.

Nudging him gently, Mickey moved the bear cub toward the raft. The cub was nervous, but he seemed to trust his new friends. He stepped into the boat and sat down next to Pluto.

"All right, here we go!" Mickey said as he stepped in. He and Minnie used their oars to push away from the rock and back into the rapids.

"Look for a good place to land on the shore!" Minnie yelled to Mickey over the rushing water.

The forest was thick along the river. Mickey and Minnie searched for a beach or another flat rock so they could safely land the raft. They passed trees, bushes, and rocky cliffs as they sped through the waves.

The raft bounced and plunged. The bear cub snuggled close to Pluto, hiding his face.

"I see a spot!" Minnie said. "There's a little beach just ahead!"

Soon they were safely on the shore. The bear cub leaped from the raft. He jumped and rolled in the sand, then ran back and forth in front of Mickey, Minnie, and Pluto.

"He's probably the first bear ever to try white-water rafting!" Mickey said, laughing.

"I don't think he liked it as much as we do! Look how happy he is to be back on land," Minnie said.

"What should we do now?" Minnie asked. "We can't just leave him here. We're so far downriver from where we found him! What if he doesn't know how to get home?"

"I suppose we can walk back through the woods to help him find his family," Mickey said, "as long as you don't mind cutting our rafting trip short."

The friends agreed that was a good plan, and they packed up all their supplies.

Mickey, Minnie, Pluto, and the bear cub headed through the
forest, following the winding path of the river. They climbed rocks,
jumped over fallen logs, and crossed through streams. Pluto and the
cub ran ahead, chasing each other around the trees.

"The sounds of the woods are so different from the roaring of the
river!" Minnie said. "I can hear birds singing, crickets chirping, and
the trickle of the little stream. It's so quiet and peaceful."

Finally, the group reached a little clearing with a rocky cliff on one
side. The bear cub ran toward a cave at the base of the cliff.

"Look!" said Minnie. "I think we found his family."

A mama bear and two cubs ran out of the cave toward the little
cub. The four licked and nuzzled one another happily.

The little cub turned back toward Mickey, Minnie, and Pluto. They smiled and waved at him from the edge of the clearing.

"Good luck, little guy!" Mickey said.

"Be careful near the river!" Minnie called.

Pluto barked good-bye, and the three friends walked into the woods while the cub followed his family into the cave.

"I'm glad we helped that little cub," Minnie said. "He looked so happy to be home."

"I know we planned to spend the day white-water rafting," Mickey said, "but I think we ended up on an even greater adventure!"

"Yes," Minnie said. "Two adventures are definitely greater than one!"

THE PET SHOW

It was a perfect day for a cookout. Mickey Mouse and his nephews, Morty and Ferdie, were preparing lunch.

Pluto barked a friendly welcome to Minnie as she joined the boys in the yard.

"I'm sorry I'm late," she said, "but I have great news. I've just been elected chairperson of the Charity Pet Show. We're raising money to build a new shelter for stray animals."

"We should enter Pluto in the show!" Morty suggested.

"Yeah! We can teach him to do tricks," said Ferdie. "Can we, Uncle Mickey? Please?"

"All right," Mickey said. "It's for a good cause."

Mickey and Minnie watched as the boys started to train Pluto.

"Roll over, Pluto," Morty said.

But Pluto just sat up and wagged his tail.

"Maybe we should show him what we want him to do," said Ferdie. Pluto watched, puzzled, as both boys rolled over in the grass.

"Let's try something that *he* likes to do," suggested Morty.

Ferdie ordered Pluto to lie down, but Pluto jumped up and began chasing his tail instead.

All week long, Morty and Ferdie tried to teach Pluto new tricks. He fetched, rolled over, lay down, begged, and shook hands . . . but only when *he* wanted to.

"Well, he *is* doing tricks," said Mickey.

"They're just not the *right* tricks," said Ferdie.

"He'll never win first prize," said Morty.

On the day of the show, Mickey and the boys took Pluto to the empty lot next door, where the show was being held. Minnie sold Mickey three tickets, then pointed happily to the cashbox.

"We've made enough to pay for the new animal shelter!" she told him.

"That's great!" cried Mickey.

What *wasn't* great was Pluto's performance.

He shook hands when he was told to sit. He rolled over when he should have jumped. He barked when he was supposed to lie down. Worst of all, when Police Chief O'Hara was choosing Best Pet of the Day, Pluto growled at him! The chief didn't know it, but he was standing right where Pluto had buried his bone!

Suddenly, the crowd heard a scream from the ticket booth.

"Help! Stop, thief! Help!"

"That's Minnie!" Mickey gasped.

"The ticket money!" Morty and Ferdie shouted.

Mickey, the boys, and Chief O'Hara ran to the booth.

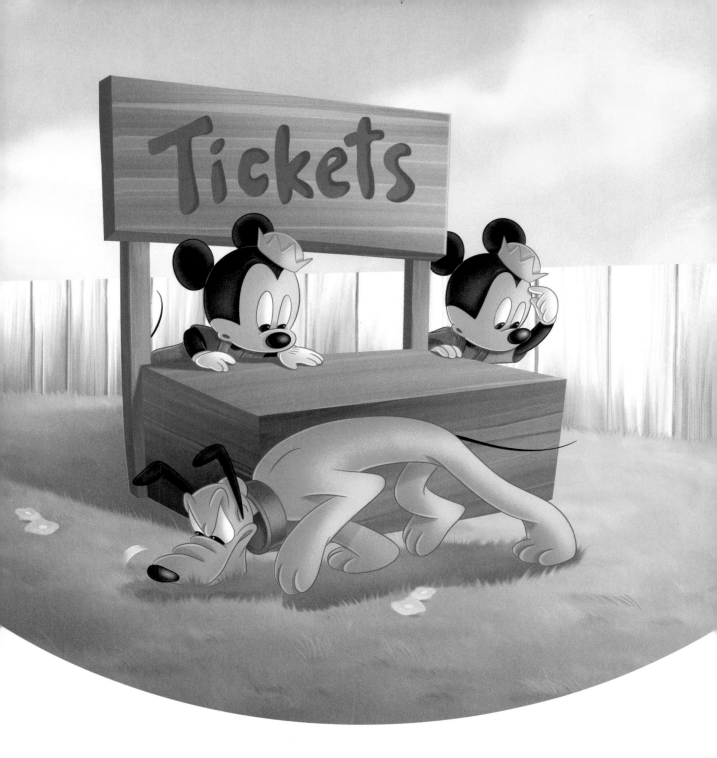

Pluto was already at the scene of the crime. He was busily sniffing around.

"All the money is gone," Minnie said. "I walked away for one minute. When I came back, I saw someone running away with the cashbox."

"What did the robber look like?" asked the chief.

Before Minnie could answer, Pluto took off. A moment later, the thief ran screaming out of the woods. He was holding on to the cashbox—and Pluto was holding on to him! Pluto growled and tugged on the thief's suspenders.

Snap! The thief's suspenders broke and shot him right into the arms of Chief O'Hara.

Later that afternoon, Chief O'Hara presented Pluto with the Four-Footed Hero medal.

The chief smiled and said, "Thanks to Pluto, every animal will have a place to go—and a chance to find a good home."

At home, Pluto waited by the front door.

"You know," said Morty, "I don't care if Pluto isn't a show dog. He's something better. He's a *hero* dog."

Mickey, Minnie, and Ferdie agreed. Then, without being told,
Pluto shook hands with everyone, because this time *he* wanted to.